# TRINITY
# GUILDHALL

GW00683629

# Drum Kit 2

## Pieces & Studies

for Trinity Guildhall examinations
2011–2013

## Grades 3 & 4

Published by
Trinity College London
89 Albert Embankment
London SE1 7TP  UK

T +44 (0)20 7820 6100
F +44 (0)20 7820 6161
E music@trinityguildhall.co.uk
www.trinityguildhall.co.uk

Copyright © 2010 Trinity College London
First impression, June 2010

Printed in England by Halstan & Co. Ltd, Amersham, Bucks.

# Trinity Guildhall graded drum kit examinations

## Introduction

The role of the drum kit player is a multifaceted one; drummers are required to play a multitude of styles (and often instruments) with conviction, flair and musical confidence. In show and cabaret playing, drummers are also required to have the ability to read and improvise. Stylistic versatility is essential to a drum kit player: the Latin American and African rhythms that are becoming increasingly influential and popular in contemporary music, strict tempo ballroom styles, contemporary pop and rock, not to mention jazz and funk, all need to be assessed. The strength of the Trinity Guildhall drum kit syllabus lies in not only challenging candidates, but in developing them towards becoming accomplished musicians.

In today's performing arena, drum kit playing is 90% accompaniment and 10% solo. It is therefore the aim of the Trinity Guildhall examination system to reflect this and to cover as broad a style base as possible over the eight grades.

Rudiment playing is assessed in a stylistic way, with candidates performing rudimental studies pertinent to the instrument. Rudiments are presented progressively for each grade and stylistic studies are performed as separate musical entities alongside the pieces.

## Drum kit examinations

Candidates are required to perform:
- a rudimental study (or studies)
- one piece from Group A (played with a backing track)
- one piece from Group B (unaccompanied)
- two supporting tests

Please refer to the current syllabus for details of supporting tests.

**Rudimental studies** are specially written pieces that involve all the rudiments set for a particular grade (see cumulative rudiments grid). These rudiments are set out at the beginning of each grade section. Candidates will be required to learn these in order to be able to play the study (or studies).

**Group A** pieces have full backing accompaniment on CD with click track where appropriate, but no drums. Candidates will be marked on their ability to interpret a typical drum chart and interact with the backing in terms of time-keeping, phrasing, soloing etc.

**Group B** pieces are unaccompanied.

## Venue equipment

At Public Centres where percussion examinations are accepted, Trinity Guildhall will normally supply a good quality five-piece drum kit that comprises:
- snare drum with adjustable drum kit (not orchestral) stand
- bass drum (18-22")
- ride cymbal (18-22")
- splash for Grades 5-8
- 3 toms (minimum) high/medium/low
- hi hat (12-14")
- crash cymbal (14-18")
- adjustable drum stool

In the case of an Examiner Visit, the visit organiser is responsible for providing the drum kit.

Drum heads should be in good condition and tuned correctly, and all stands and pedals should be in good mechanical order. Larger kits may be used, as may flat drum kits, but electric drum kits may not. Double bass drum pedals may be used in solos and fills if desired. Candidates wishing to use their own kits may only do so at the discretion of the Centre Representative, and the setting up of the kit must not be allowed to interfere with the timing of the session.

In all cases candidates must provide their own sticks, which must be in good condition and suitable for the repertoire being performed. When the examination entry is made, it should be clearly indicated on the entry form if a drum kit candidate is left handed.

For all drum kit grades it is the responsibility of the person signing the entry form to ensure that suitable playback equipment for CDs is provided. Some centres may provide this equipment and the applicant should contact the centre well in advance to confirm the arrangements. In all cases, arrangements (about power supply, equipment insurance etc.) must be agreed with the Centre Representative.

The equipment must be of good quality, comprising CD player with track search facility and good quality loudspeakers that are capable of reproducing the volume required for comfortable playalong (c. 20W). 'Ghetto blasters' are to be discouraged unless they have sufficient power to enable comfortable monitoring of CD for playalong or are connected to an external amplifier. Headphones may be worn by the candidate as long as there is a separate amplification route that enables the examiner to hear both drum kit and backing adequately.

Please note that a percussion-equipped warm-up room is not supplied for percussion examinations.

Trinity Guildhall recommends the use of ear defenders by candidates and examiners for the performance of drum kit repertoire for health and safety reasons. These should be used for all pieces and studies.

# Drum kit rudiments

| Rudiment / Grade | Grade 1 | Grade 2 | Grade 3 | Grade 4 | Grade 5 | Grade 6 | Grade 7 | Grade 8 |
|---|---|---|---|---|---|---|---|---|
| Single strokes | ✓ | ✓ | ✓ | ✓ | ✓ | ✓ | ✓ | ✓ |
| Double strokes | ✓ | ✓ | ✓ | ✓ | ✓ | ✓ | ✓ | ✓ |
| Single paradiddle | ✓ | ✓ | ✓ | ✓ | ✓ | ✓ | ✓ | ✓ |
| Flam | | ✓ | ✓ | ✓ | ✓ | ✓ | ✓ | ✓ |
| Drag | | ✓ | ✓ | ✓ | ✓ | ✓ | ✓ | ✓ |
| Four stroke ruff | | ✓ | ✓ | ✓ | ✓ | ✓ | ✓ | ✓ |
| Five stroke roll | | | ✓ | ✓ | ✓ | ✓ | ✓ | ✓ |
| Seven stroke roll | | | ✓ | ✓ | ✓ | ✓ | ✓ | ✓ |
| Nine stroke roll | | | ✓ | ✓ | ✓ | ✓ | ✓ | ✓ |
| Flam tap | | | | ✓ | ✓ | ✓ | ✓ | ✓ |
| Flam accent | | | | ✓ | ✓ | ✓ | ✓ | ✓ |
| Flamacue | | | | ✓ | ✓ | ✓ | ✓ | ✓ |
| Flam paradiddle | | | | ✓ | ✓ | ✓ | ✓ | ✓ |
| Double paradiddle | | | | ✓ | ✓ | ✓ | ✓ | ✓ |
| Paradiddle-diddle | | | | ✓ | ✓ | ✓ | ✓ | ✓ |
| Drag and stroke | | | | | ✓ | ✓ | ✓ | ✓ |
| Double drag and stroke | | | | | ✓ | ✓ | ✓ | ✓ |
| Drag paradiddle | | | | | ✓ | ✓ | ✓ | ✓ |
| Single ratamacue | | | | | ✓ | ✓ | ✓ | ✓ |
| Double ratamacue | | | | | ✓ | ✓ | ✓ | ✓ |
| Triple ratamacue | | | | | ✓ | ✓ | ✓ | ✓ |
| Triple paradiddle | | | | | | ✓ | ✓ | ✓ |
| Reverse paradiddle | | | | | | ✓ | ✓ | ✓ |
| Pata fla fla | | | | | | | ✓ | ✓ |
| Swiss army triplet | | | | | | | ✓ | ✓ |
| Inward paradiddle | | | | | | | ✓ | ✓ |

# Drum kit notation key

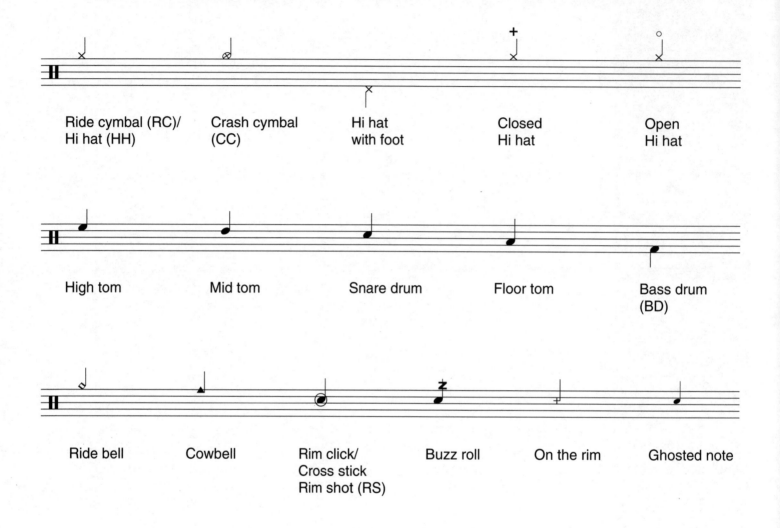

# Performance notes

## General note for both grades

Where a crash cymbal appears at the start of a bar and is followed by one-bar repeat signs ( ![repeat sign] ), the crash cymbal should **not** be played in the repeat bars. This is universally accepted as standard drum kit notation and it is the aim of the Trinity Guildhall syllabus to encourage students to become familiar with what they will be confronted with in the real world of drum kit performance.

**All** repeats, including those within *da capo* and *dal segno* sections, should be observed in drum kit examinations.

## Grade 3

### Dave Webster        Grade 3 Rudimental Study no. 1

Bars 1–3 can be started on either hand depending on whether left or right handed. In bar 3 the ascending tom notes can all be played with the same hand, but should display evenness of tone and volume. Bar 4 features flams and drags. These should be executed alternately, i.e. if beat 2 is played ʀʟ, beat 3 should start ʟʟʀ and beat 4 ʀʟ. In the first time bar the two left-hand beats should be ghosted to bring out the accents. If left handed, the sticking can be reversed. The roll in the second time bar should be even with a marked *diminuendo* and *crescendo* building to the single stroke pattern around the kit. Dynamic control of the paradiddle and double strokes in the next two bars is crucial. In the last two bars, sticking can be reversed if left handed.

### Dave Webster        Grade 3 Rudimental Study no. 2

This study uses a combination of five, seven and nine stroke rolls, within a semiquaver/sixteenth-note funk groove. Bar 10 must use seven stroke rolls beginning on either hand.

### Pete Riley/
### Andy Staples        Meanstreak

The idea behind this piece was to evoke the rhythmic syncopation typical of rock bands such as AC/DC, where the majority of the rhythmic movement comes from the guitars while the drums remain fairly static. In this case the groove is based around a crotchet/quarter-note feel played in the right hand, while the bass drum occasionally follows the guitars. This is most noticeable during the A and B sections where the first bass drum of each two-bar pattern is played on the 'and' of beat 1. Be sure to keep the hi hat slightly open to create a trashy rock feel. The rhythmic notation in bars 1–7 and 54–62 can be orchestrated as the player feels appropriate. Actual notated fills should be played as written.

### Ben Beer        Soup

This is a laid-back piece with varied snare and tom patterns and fills.

### Andrew Tween/
### Jonathan Taylor  Kiss of a Seal

This piece is a musical pastiche of a track from the artist Seal. It is important to consider the dynamic build of the track, the rising and falling of the sections in volume and musical intensity. The drum part is created to help the intensity, using different colours from the snare (cross stick/stick on skin) to variations of hi hat colour (closed/half open/open) that lead into different sections of the piece. The first big 'epic' fill on bar 25 leads on to the ride which gives a sense of 'openness' on the kit as the track opens out musically. Be careful not to rush the fills and try to play sensitively where the music dictates.

### Keith Bartlett        A Right Old Rumba

The Rumba is a very popular Latin American dance and the first two bars clearly demonstrate its unique rhythmic pattern. Note how the bass drum plays on beat 4 as well as beats 1 and 3. Observe the dynamics carefully and make sure that any accents you encounter are played in a musical and not overpowering manner. Take time to experiment with the rim click passages in order to produce the most resonant sound possible.

## George Double      Big Foot Boogie

The main theme of this piece is played on bass drum. The quavers/eighth notes on the snare should sit supportively underneath and must never be allowed to dominate. Play out a little more in the half-time groove at bar 17. Take note of the roll directions in the footnote.

## Mark Aldous      Triplicity

Triplicity is a study in triplet to duplet changes in rhythm within a $\frac{3}{4}$ Latin-waltz style. The key to a successful performance is ensuring a firm crotchet/quarter-note pulse in the feet (HH and BD). A light Latin tone is suggested for this piece.

# Grade 4

## Dave Webster      Grade 4 Rudimental Study no. 1

An even $\frac{12}{8}$ feel is needed here, not too rushed. Getting the tempo wrong at the start will cause difficulties in the closing sections.

Use alternate sticking in bars 2 and 6 for the flamacues and in bars 4 and 8 for the flam accents. The change in time signature should 'sit' in a heavy rock feel, again not rushed, and use alternate sticking in bar 10, flam taps. The two repeat bars with the flam paradiddles need to be played in time with the two cymbal accents played R L or L R (this is most effective if two crash cymbals are used). The final two bars rely heavily on the accents to provide the right feel.

## Dave Webster      Grade 4 Rudimental Study no. 2

This study should have a lilting Afro-Cuban feel. Bars 1 and 2 use double paradiddle; bars 3 and 4 use paradiddle-diddle.

## Paul Clarvis      When Stanley Met Astrid

Be sure that the shaker sound balances and blends with the kit, and that your feet underpin, but don't overshadow your brush work.

Recommended listening: Getz/Gilberto, Sinatra/Jobim and Orquestra Mahatma. For an example of brush playing, listen to *Starry, Starry Night* on Village Life label.

## Neil Robinson/
### John Dutton      Movin' On

A blues shuffle piece with phrasing and solo section.

## Troy Miller      St Lucia Strut

All fills on snare drum can be played as 'rim shots' for a timbale-type sound. Don't be afraid to make improvised elements simple and focused on the 'pocket'.

Recommended listening: Peter Tosh, Bob Marley, Toots and the Maytals.

## Paul Francis      Monchique

This piece is based on semiquavers/sixteenth notes starting with a four-bar groove with syncopated bass drum. This leads into the next section, which moves around the toms then incorporates the snare before returning to two bars of groove. The final section has linear independence between hands and bass drum. Linear means no two surfaces are played together.

Check out DVDs of Greg Bissonette and Steve Smith for examples of this style of playing. It is advisable to practise this at a slow tempo first.

## Rick Hudson      Groove Tree

A rock-based piece that uses a 3-2 bossa nova clave. In bars 13-18 a 2-3 clave pattern is used. From bar 29 try to keep the semiquaver/sixteenth-note pulse in your head. This will help with coordination and 'feel' within this section.

## Mark Aldous      Samba for One

The challenge of this piece is to evoke an authentic Samba feel and atmosphere using the drum kit. The piece opens with a Caixa-like intro where the accents show the main rhythmic identity of the piece. The quasi-Agogo bell part in the ride cymbal can be achieved by using the shoulder and tip of the stick as indicated. In trying to emulate the correct sound you are encouraged to research authentic Samba bands.

# Grade 3 Rudiments

You will need to learn the rudiments up to Grade 2 and the following to be able to play the Grade 3 Rudimental Studies.

**Five stroke roll**

**Seven stroke roll**

**Nine stroke roll**

Note that the tempo must be increased to establish rebounded rolls.

Both studies must be performed in the examination.

# Grade 3
# Rudimental Study no. 1

Dave Webster

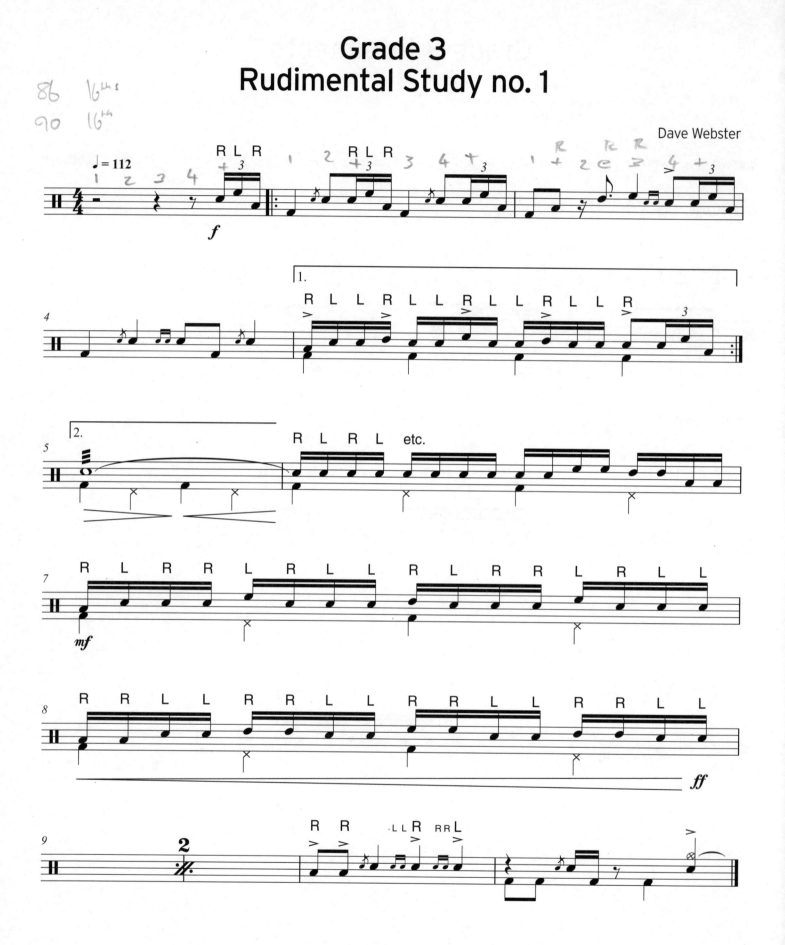

**Remember to look at the Performance Notes on pages 5-6**

Both studies must be performed in the examination.

*Practise doubles to click*
*80 bpm*
*100 bpm*
*110 bpm*
*120 bpm*

# Grade 3
# Rudimental Study no. 2

Dave Webster

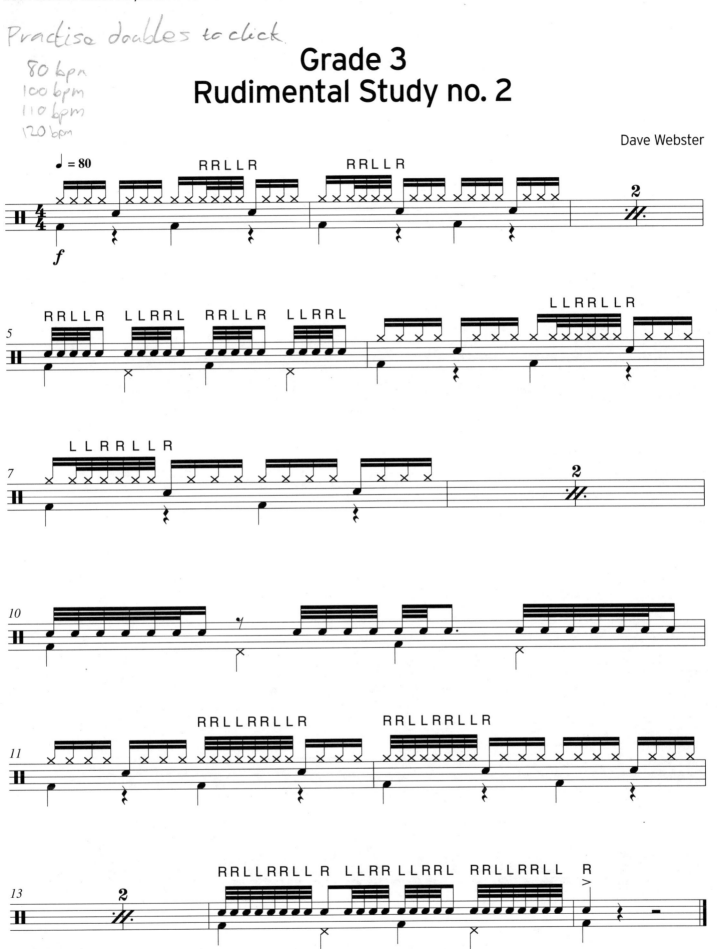

**Remember to look at the Performance Notes on pages 5-6**

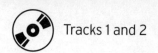
Tracks 1 and 2

# Meanstreak

Pete Riley/Andy Staples

= performer's choice of drum(s) to be played using rhythm shown.          φ = Half-open HH.

Play with dynamics appropriate to the music.

Remember to look at the Performance Notes on pages 5-6

# Soup

Ben Beer

**Remember to look at the Performance Notes on pages 5-6**

# Kiss of a Seal

Andrew Tween/Jonathan Taylor

φ = Half-open HH.

**Remember to look at the Performance Notes on pages 5-6**

# A Right Old Rumba

Keith Bartlett

**Remember to look at the Performance Notes on pages 5-6**

# Big Foot Boogie

George Double

Remember to look at the Performance Notes on pages 5-6

# Triplicity

Mark Aldous

**Remember to look at the Performance Notes on pages 5-6**

*  ♩
= Crash bell.

# Grade 4 Rudiments

You will need to learn the rudiments up to Grade 3 and the following to be able to play the Grade 4 Rudimental Studies.

**Flam tap**

**Flam accent**

**Flamacue**

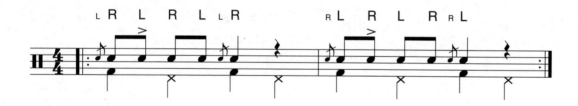

## Flam paradiddle

## Double paradiddle

## Paradiddle-diddle

Both studies must be performed in the examination.

# Grade 4
# Rudimental Study no. 1

Dave Webster

**Remember to look at the Performance Notes on pages 5-6**

22

Both studies must be performed in the examination.

# Grade 4
# Rudimental Study no. 2

Dave Webster

**Remember to look at the Performance Notes on pages 5-6**

# When Stanley met Astrid

Paul Clarvis

Play with dynamics appropriate to the music.

\* Play with brush in a right-left 'scrubbing' effect. The brush is in contact with the drum head at all times. The following snare strokes are thus played with the other hand.

= performer's choice of drum(s) to be played using rhythm shown.

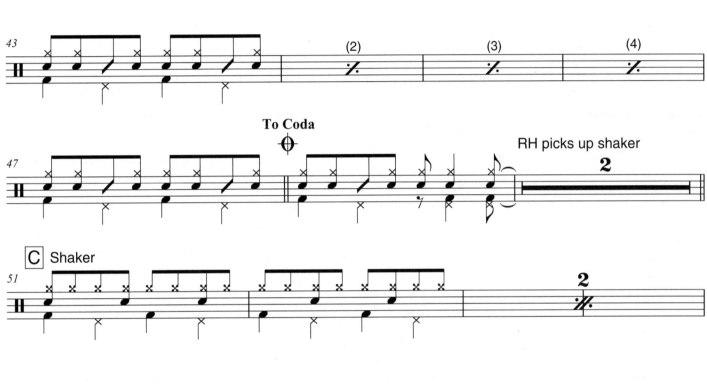

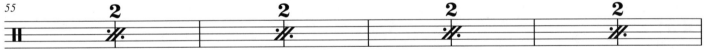

**Remember to look at the Performance Notes on pages 5-6**

# Movin' On

Neil Robinson/John Dutton

**Remember to look at the Performance Notes on pages 5-6**

(Guitar solo)

# St Lucia Strut

Troy Miller

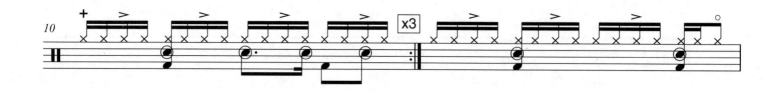

**Remember to look at the Performance Notes on pages 5-6**

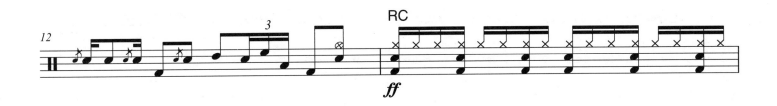

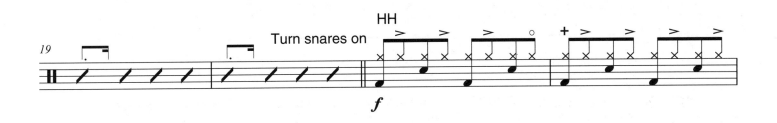

# Monchique

Paul Francis

**Remember to look at the Performance Notes on pages 5-6**

# Groove Tree

Rick Hudson

**Remember to look at the Performance Notes on pages 5-6**

# Samba for One

Mark Aldous

* Quasi-Agogo bell.   ** = Tip of stick.

**Remember to look at the Performance Notes on pages 5-6**